Barnacle Is BORED

For Mom and Dad, with love and gratefulness.

ISBN 978-0-545-90789-7
10 9 8 7 6 5 4 3 2 1   16 17 18 19 20

Printed in the U.S.A.   08
First printing 2016

Book design by Steve Ponzo

Barnacle Is BORED

Jonathan Fenske

Scholastic Inc.

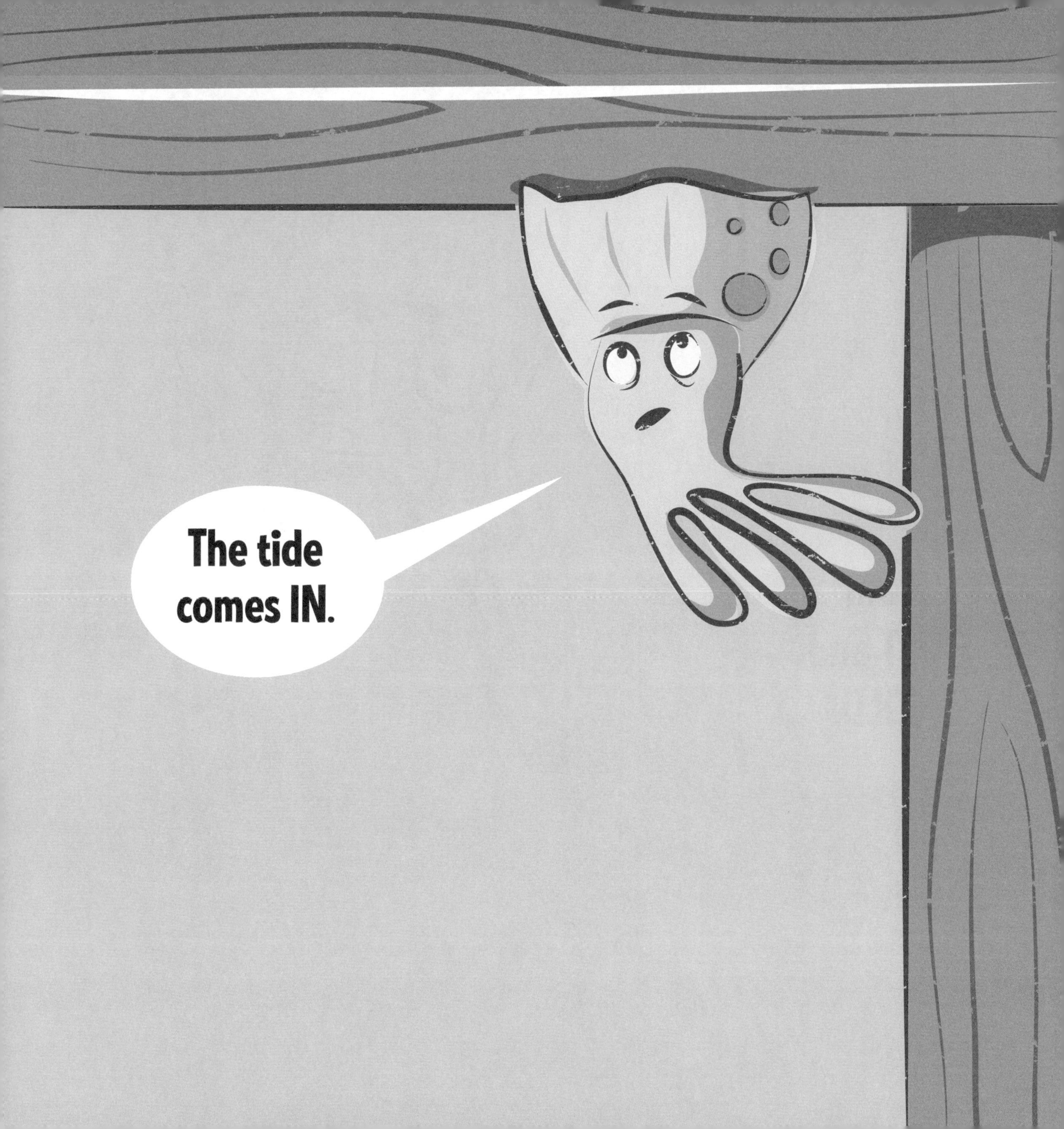
The tide comes IN.

The sun comes UP.

The sun comes UP again.

Waves roll OVER me.

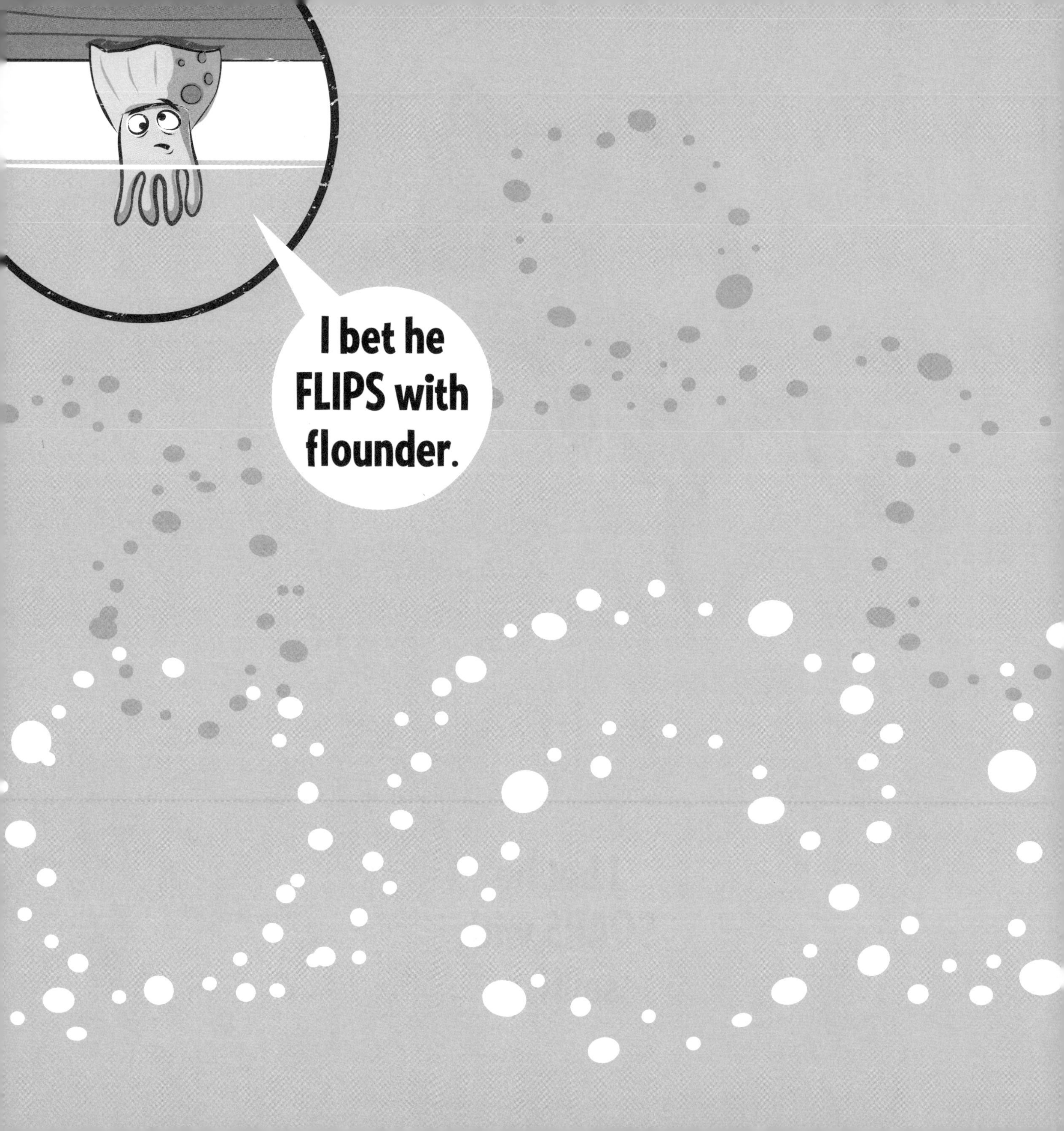
I bet he FLIPS with flounder.

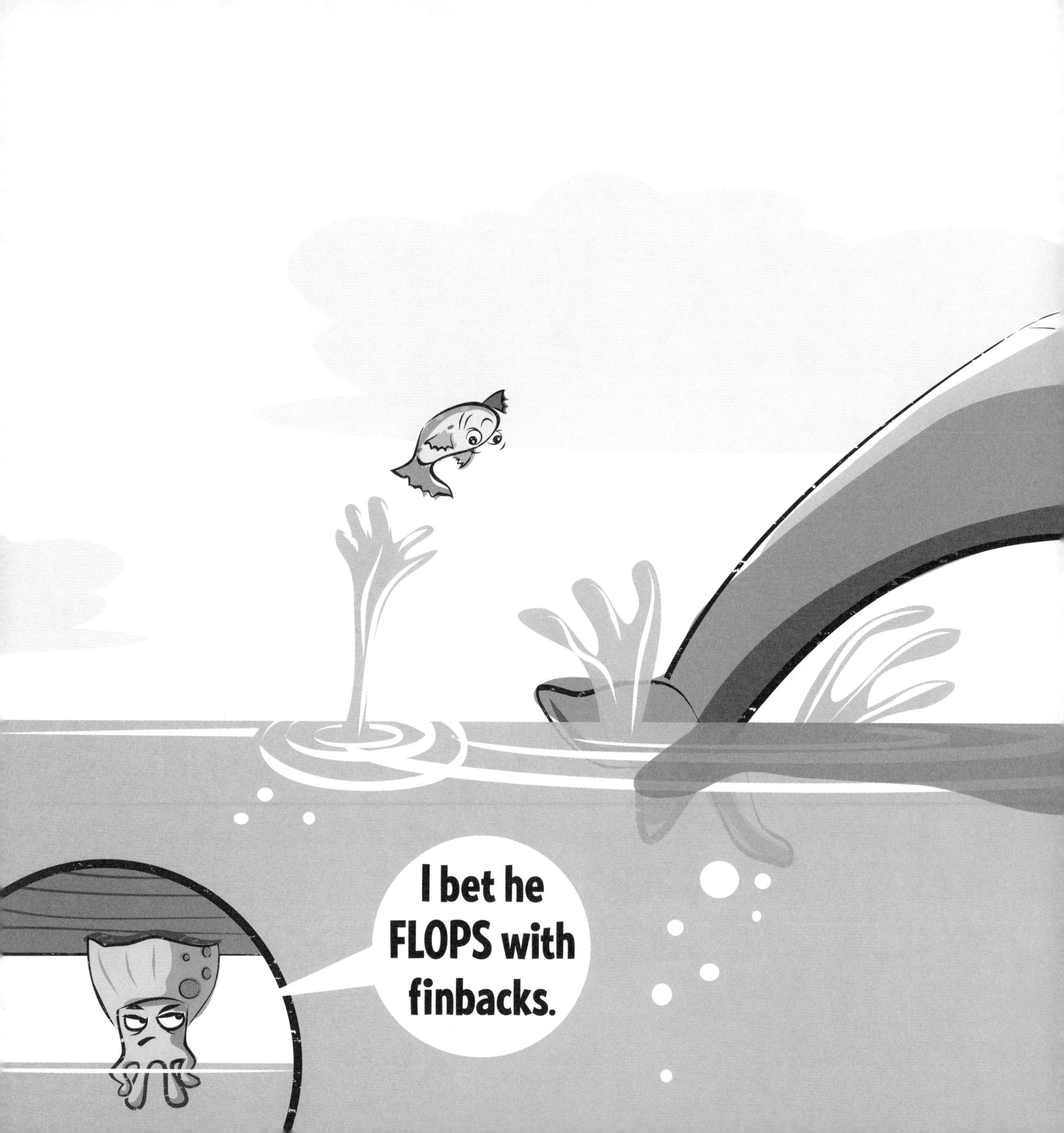
I bet he FLOPS with finbacks.

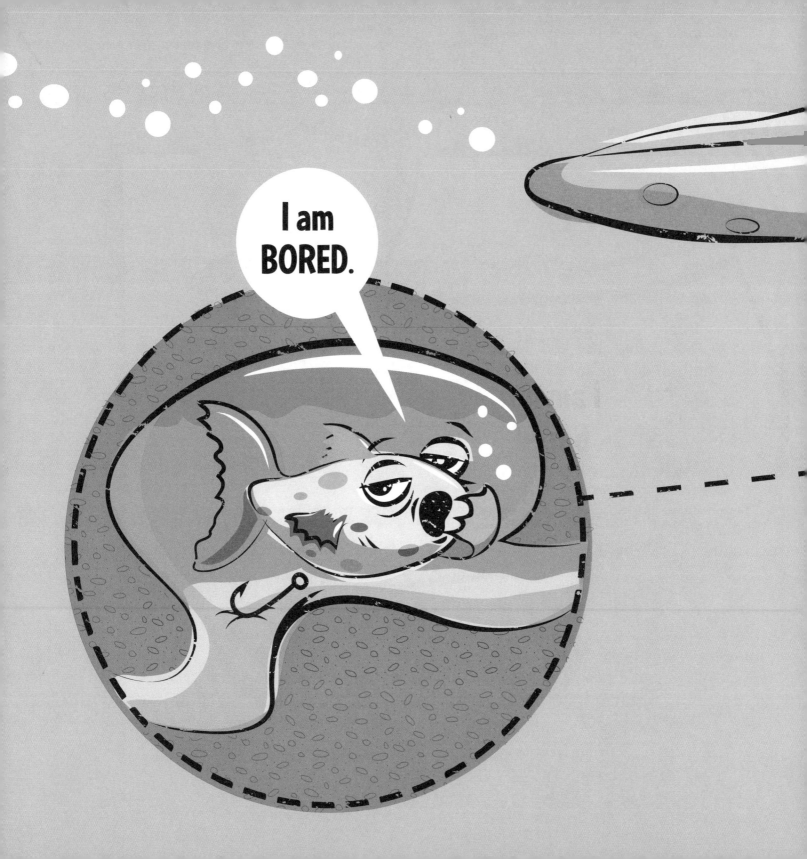